Contents

Introduction

Abacus Foundation

Since the introduction of the Foundation Stage and the publication of the related *Curriculum Guidance* in May 2000, teachers in playgroups, nurseries and reception classes now have both curriculum content and a set of principles to inform their teaching. The *Curriculum Guidance for the Foundation Stage* designates six areas of learning for children, one of which is 'Mathematical development'. Each area is outlined in some detail and provides a series of 'stepping stones'. These are intended to help practitioners plan a progression of activities to allow children to achieve the Early Learning Goals.

The **Abacus Foundation** materials are designed and written to support teachers with planning and teaching to match the *Curriculum Guidance for the Foundation Stage*. Two books are provided at each level (F1 for 3- to 4-year-olds, F2 for 4- to 5-year-olds) – a Teachers' Resource Book and an Activity Book. The Teachers' Resource Book comprises a complete series of weekly plans which include suggestions for daily 'on-the-rug' large group teacher-led activities, and outlines of differentiated ideas for teacher-initiated small group or paired activities (these are expanded in detail in the Activity Book), as well as opportunities for learning through structured play activities.

The weekly plans in the Teachers' Resource Book, backed up by the bank of activities in the Activity Book, save teachers time by offering a balanced and adaptable starting point, and allow them to cease re-inventing the wheel by continually writing their own material. The plans are linked to the 'Mathematical development' strand in the *Curriculum Guidance for the Foundation Stage* and provide a comprehensive two-year programme leading clearly to the Early Learning Goals for mathematics.

Activity Book

The **Abacus Foundation** Activity Books for F1 and F2 are an ideal resource for all those working with children aged 3 to 5. The activities can be used in school, in a playgroup or nursery, or even at home. Some are suitable for more direct or formal teaching, and others will slot effectively into the context of a play activity. Most of the activities can be used either with one child, pairs or groups of up to five children. The weekly activities are differentiated to enable teachers to plan efficiently, and any practitioner to select appropriate activities for different children. All the activities in this large bank are flexible and can easily be adapted to accommodate a range of specific circumstances, making this book a perfect dip-in resource to reinforce children's mathematical skills as they learn.

The activities in this book are provided in two sections – differentiated activities linked directly to the weekly plans in the Teachers' Resource Book, followed by a bank of further activities arranged by mathematical topic. The Activity Book can be used in a variety of ways:
- to find an activity for immediate use
- to plan activities for the next half term in conjunction with the weekly plans in the Teachers' Resource Book
- to provide an activity for parents and children to share – either at home or in school
- to select activities by topic linked to the Early Learning Goals.

The differentiated activities, ordered by term and week, are outlined in brief on the matching weekly plans, then expanded in more detail in this book. They give suggestions for Easy, Medium and Hard activities to match the objectives of each weekly plan. This enables teachers to select activities to suit particular groups of children and also to plan a progression of activities throughout the year.

The activities are intended for use in a teaching situation, when a practitioner is working with a small group on a teacher-initiated activity, but some are also appropriate for more informal learning situations where the children are engaged in play activities and choose what to do themselves. The majority of the activities need little preparation and are suitable for learning support assistants or parents to use within or outside the classroom context. Each activity includes the following information:

- Learning points to assist the practitioner in directing the children and making informal assessments. In the case of the differentiated activities, these learning points draw directly on the objectives from the appropriate weekly plan.
- A list of materials required for the activity. It is likely that most of these will be freely available in the classroom ensuring that prior preparation time is kept to a minimum.
- Detailed instructions on how to run the activity, including suggestions for questions to ask the children.

Classroom management

Good early years practice involves the setting up of a wide variety of informal learning situations, and also some direct teaching in several different contexts. Play is crucial, but so is demonstrating or modelling how to do something. Young children's development relies upon the regular supply of a varied diet of educational activity. The most successful – and also the most appealing – educational settings are those which provide both free play as well as short sessions of direct teaching. 'On the rug' time or 'Circle time' of teacher-led activities with a large group, or teacher-initiated activities with a small group, allow teachers to demonstrate particular skills very effectively. Equally, becoming an 'expert play partner' helps the practitioner offer specific learning opportunities for children, e.g. recognising colours or comparing and sorting when playing in the water tray or sand pit. In any of these contexts, children will learn not only the maths in question, but also how to persevere, concentrate and work with others.

In accordance with the principles of the *Curriculum Guidance for the Foundation Stage*, the **Abacus Foundation** materials allow for children to be taught and learn in a variety of contexts. Some areas of mathematics are best taught directly, to a large group. Others are better suited to teaching a small group, and some skills, such as writing numerals, require attention on an individual level. A variety of all these teaching – and learning – methods can be used at different times for most skills. Some, however, cannot be directly taught, and are best acquired in the course of an informal activity, i.e. a structured play activity that is initiated or led by the child.

The following table categorises the mathematical skills covered in the Foundation Stage into suitable learning situations.

	Large group	Small group	Individuals or pairs
Taught directly	• Counting • Chanting number names in order • Counting objects/events/movements • Number rhymes • Days of the week • Shape names	• Counting objects • Matching a spoken numeral to quantity • Adding 1 or 2 more • Partitioning a set • Comparing lengths	• Matching numerals to sets • Writing numerals • Matching days of the week to special events
Learned informally	• Sorting shapes • Colours • Recognising large numbers • Positions		

Term 1

Week 1

Action line
Easy

• *Counting to 10*
Number track (1 to 10), interlocking cubes
Taking turns, each child chooses a number on the track. Encourage them to find their chosen number by counting to it along the track. The children choose an action to perform that number of times, e.g. hop six times to match the number 6. As the child hops, the other children count to check the number. If correct, the child who hopped wins a cube. The children continue playing until one of them has collected ten cubes.

Moving on
Medium

• *Saying the next number to a given number*
Number track (1 to 20), a coin, counters
Give each child a counter to place on number 1 on the track. The children take turns to spin a coin. If it lands tails, they move their counter forwards one space; if it lands heads, they move forwards two spaces. Encourage the children to say the number they land on. If the child can say the next number, they can move on an extra space. Otherwise they move back three spaces (or back to 1). The winner is the first child to reach 20.

Next-door cards
Hard

• *Recognising the number 1 more and 1 less than a given number*
Number cards (1 to 10)
With the children in groups of three, shuffle the number cards and deal out three to each child. Place the last card face up. The children take turns to put down a card that is 1 more or 1 less than the card on the table. If they are unable to do this, they miss a turn. The first child to lay down all their cards is the winner.

Week 2

Jigsaw count
Easy

- *Counting to 20*

A jigsaw, card (or old greetings cards), felt-tipped pens, scissors

Give each pair of children a jigsaw. Ask them to count the number of pieces and complete the jigsaw. Ask the children to draw a picture on a piece of card. When they have finished, cut the picture into pieces and mix them up. Ask the children to put the picture back together. Alternatively, use an old greetings card.

How many pencils?
Medium

- *Beginning to record numbers to 20*
- *Estimating quantities to 20*

Pencils, a mug, number track (1 to 20), interlocking cubes

Ask a child to take a handful of pencils and place them in a mug. Write the children's names and ask them to estimate the number of pencils. Encourage them to record their estimate next to their name. Let them refer to the number track if necessary, counting along to find the appropriate number. Count out the pencils one at a time. Look at the estimated numbers and give the child with the nearest estimate a cube. Repeat several times.

Tall towers
Hard

- *Counting up to 10 objects*

Number cards (1 to 10), interlocking cubes, counters

Shuffle the number cards and deal one to each child. *Who has the biggest/smallest number?* Ask the children to take a number of cubes to match their card and make a tower with them. *Who do you think will have the tallest/shortest towers? Why?* Give the child with the tallest tower a counter. Repeat several times until one child has five counters.

Week 3

Hidden shapes
Easy

- *Identifying squares and circles*

A large book, a picture of a circle and a square, different-sized card circles and squares

Show the children the pictures of the circle and the square. Ask them if they can remember the names of the shapes and write them on the pictures. Encourage them to describe the shape's properties. Hold a book upright so that some card circles and squares can be hidden behind it. Select a child to slide a shape under the book into the view of the other children. Tell the children to put up their hands as soon as they recognise the shape and tell you how they recognised it. Repeat several times.

Shape patterns
Medium

- *Recognising and naming 2-d shapes*

A variety of plastic 2-d shapes

Set out some different 2-d shapes in a line. Give the children some shapes and ask them to copy the line. Discuss and, if possible, name each shape. *Can you take away the squares from your line?* Check, then ask them to replace the squares. Repeat for other shapes.

Drawing shapes
Hard

- *Recognising different 2-d shapes*

A variety of plastic 2-d shapes, Blu-tack

Ask the children to choose a shape and draw round it, using the Blu-tack to hold it in place. Then encourage them to try to draw the same shape free-hand. As the children draw their shape, discuss the shape's properties with them.

Week 4

One more brick
Easy

- *Adding 1 to a number up to 10*

A number track (1 to 12), building bricks

In turn, ask each child to choose a number on the track. They then take a matching number of bricks. *How many bricks will you have if you take one more?* If they give the correct answer, they keep the bricks. If not, they put them back in the pile. After six turns each, let the children make a model with their bricks.

Counting pebbles
Medium

- *Adding 1 to a number up to 10*

A dice (labelled 5 to 10, opposite sides add to 15), several pebbles

The children take turns to roll the dice, count out the corresponding number of pebbles and make a line with them. *How many pebbles will you have if you take one more?* If they give the correct answer, they keep one pebble and put the rest back in the pile. The children continue until one of them has six pebbles.

Collecting bricks
Hard

- *Adding 1 to a number up to 10*

A number track (1 to 20), counters, a coin, building bricks

Give each child a counter. Ask the children to put them on number 1 on the number track. In turn, the children spin a coin and move their counter accordingly: heads move forwards one space, tails move forwards two spaces. The children look at the number they land on and take that number of bricks plus one. So if they land on 3, they take four bricks. If they make a mistake, they must put the bricks back. The children continue until they reach the end of the track.

Week 5

Towers of 7
Easy

- *Adding by partitioning a set*

Red and yellow building bricks

Give the children a pile of red and yellow bricks and ask each child to make a tower of seven bricks using both colours. They count the number of red and yellow bricks in each tower and say the number sentence, e.g. *Six and one makes seven.* Encourage the children to make as many different towers as they can.

Duck ponds
Medium

• *Adding by partitioning a set*

Two cardboard or mirror 'ponds', seven plastic ducks

Place the two 'ponds' on the floor close to each other. Invite a child to distribute the seven ducks over the ponds. Record the matching number sentence, e.g. 5 + 2 = 7, and encourage the children to say it. Let another child distribute the ducks in a different way. Continue until all the possible combinations have been found. Repeat the activity using either six or eight ducks.

Money purses
Hard

• *Adding by partitioning a set*

Two purses, 1p coins

Divide the children into pairs and give each pair several 1p coins and two purses. Ask them to find as many different ways as possible of distributing eight of the coins between the purses. Write the number sentence for each variation, e.g. 6p + 2p = 8p, and encourage the children to say it. Ask the children to try the same activity using 2p and 5p coins as well.

Week 6

Tall toys
Easy

• *Comparing heights*

Post-it notes, strips of paper, Blu-tack, toys

Paste three strips of paper horizontally at different heights on a cupboard door. Write the names of toys on Post-it notes. The children take turns to hold a toy against the cupboard door and stick Post-it notes at the appropriate height for each one. *Which toys are taller than the lowest strip but shorter than the middle strip? Which are taller than the top strip?* Help the children to line up the toys in order of height.

A fishy scene
Medium

• *Comparing the length of three objects*

Paper fish in different lengths, glue, blue paper

Invite each child to choose three paper fish of different lengths, one short, one long and one between the two. Let them stick the fish in order of length onto some blue paper to make a fishy scene.

Creepy crawlies
Hard

• *Comparing the length of three objects*
Pictures of insects, glue

Invite the children to choose three pictures of insects and arrange them in order of length on a piece of paper. When they are satisfied that the order is correct, they glue them onto the paper.

Week 7

Tall boxes
Easy

• *Comparing tall and short*
A selection of boxes

Show the children the boxes and pick out one that is tall and one that is short. Ask the children to point to the taller box. Put the boxes back with the others and ask the children to point to the tallest box. In turn, ask each child to choose two of the boxes and say which is the taller one.

Skyscrapers
Medium

• *Comparing tall and short*
Pictures of buildings of various sizes

Show the children the pictures. Together, sort them into tall and short buildings. Let the children draw a picture of either a tall or short building. Display them in two distinct groups.

Make a box
Hard

• *Comparing tall and short*
Nets of cuboids, sticky tape, adhesive shapes, coloured pencils

Show the children how to put together one of the nets to make either a tall or a short box. Let the children choose a net for each type of box and decorate the outer sides. Then help them to make up their boxes. Let the children group them together as tall and short boxes.

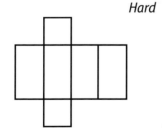

Week 8

Brick towers
Easy

• *Discussing who has less and who has more*
Building bricks, a box

Give each child twenty building bricks so that they can appreciate what that number of bricks looks and feels like. Put all the bricks back into the box. Divide the children into pairs and ask them to take a handful of bricks each. *Who has more bricks?* Let each child make a tower with their bricks to see who has taken more. The children then count the number of bricks in each tower.

Largest numbers
Medium

• *Comparing two numbers*

A number track (1 to 20), a coin, counters, interlocking cubes

The children place their counters on number 1 on the number track. In turn, the children spin the coin and move their counter accordingly: heads move forwards three spaces, tails move forwards two spaces. When they have each moved their counter, they compare the numbers of the spaces they are on. *Who is on the largest number? Who is furthest along the track?* The child on the largest number takes a cube. They continue until they reach the end of the track. The winner is the child with the most cubes.

Comparing cards
Hard

• *Comparing two numbers*

Number cards (1 to 30), interlocking cubes

Shuffle the cards and place them face up in a pile. Ask each child to take a card. Compare the numbers on the cards. The child with the largest number takes a cube. Collect the cards, reshuffle them and repeat several times. The child with the most cubes is the winner.

Week 9

Bead lines
Easy

• *Counting forwards and backwards to and from 10*

Number cards (1 to 10), beads, laces

Ask each child to thread ten beads onto a lace which is knotted at one end. Give them a set of number cards each and ask them to place the number 10 card in front of them. Each child then removes a bead from their lace and places it on the card. They count the remaining beads and find the matching number card. They continue until they have laid out all the cards from 10 to 1.

Counting back
Medium

• *Counting forwards and backwards to and from 10*
Number cards (1 to 10), 1p coins

Shuffle the cards and place them in a pile face down. In turn, the children take a card and count back from that number to 1. If they are correct, give them a coin. The card is replaced at the bottom of the pile and the children continue until one of them has collected 10p.

Down the line
Hard

• *Counting forwards and backwards to and from 20*
A number track (1 to 20), counters, a coin, 1p coins

The children place their counters on 20 on the number track. In turn, they spin a coin and move their counter accordingly: heads move two spaces backwards, tails move one space backwards. Before they move their counter, the children must say the number they will land on. If they are correct, give them a coin. They continue until they reach number 1. *Who has collected the most coins?*

Week 10

Sets of shapes
Easy

• *Sorting 2-d shapes*
Plastic 2-d shapes (squares, circles, triangles, rectangles), labels ('square', 'circle', 'triangle', 'rectangle')

Place the shapes at random on a table. Read the labels to the children and place them near the shapes. Invite the children to sort the shapes and place them next to the appropriate label.

Shape lines
Medium

• *Beginning to name rectangles and triangles*
• *Rehearsing naming squares and circles*
Plastic 2-d shapes (squares, circles, triangles, rectangles)

Using all four different shapes, create a line of shapes with a repeating pattern. Encourage the children to copy the pattern, naming the shapes as they place them. How many times can they repeat the same pattern?

Drawing shapes
Hard

• *Beginning to name rectangles and triangles*
• *Rehearsing naming squares and circles*
Plastic 2-d shapes (squares, circles, triangles, rectangles), coloured pencils

Ask the children to draw round each of the four shapes and to colour each one in a different colour. As they draw the shapes, discuss their properties and ensure that they can name each shape.

Week 11

How much money?
Easy

• *Counting up to ten 1p coins*
Number cards (1 to 10), 1p coins

Place a large pile of 1p coins on a table and ask each child to take a few. The children then count their coins to find out how many pennies they have. They then find a number card to match the number of coins.

Buying biscuits
Medium

- *Recognising that we use coins for buying and selling*
- *Counting up to ten 1p coins*

Different types of biscuit, plates, price labels, 1p coins

Put each type of biscuit on a different plate and give each one a different price, e.g. chocolate 9p, raisin 6p, cream 7p, plain 3p. Give each child ten 1p coins. In turn, ask them to choose a biscuit and pay for it with their coins. They then draw their biscuit. Help them to write the price of it next to the drawing.

What can we buy?
Hard

- *Recognising coins*
- *Recognising that pounds will buy more than pennies*

Plastic coins (all denominations), long strips of paper, sticky tape

Show the children each coin in turn and discuss what they can buy with each one. Fold the strips of paper to make zig-zag books and give one to each child. Invite the children to stick one of each coin in their book and to draw, on the page opposite to each coin, a picture of something they could buy with that coin.

Week 12

One-minute models
Easy

- *Understanding that we can measure time*

Building bricks, a one-minute sand timer

Give each child a pile of bricks. Activate the timer and ask the children to make a model using as many bricks as possible before the sand runs out. At the end of one minute, let the children show the rest of the class their one-minute models.

Minute rolls
Medium

- *Counting the number of times something happens in one minute*

Several sets of number cards (1 to 6), a dice, a one-minute sand timer

Activate the timer and ask each child in turn to roll the dice and pass it on. The children take a number card to match the number rolled. At the end of one minute, count the cards taken to find out how many times the dice was rolled. *Which number was rolled most often?*

What time is it?
Hard

• *Understanding that we can measure time*
• *Recognising the hours on an analogue clock*
An analogue clock with movable hands

Set the clock hands on a particular hour. Discuss how to read the time. *What time is this?* Ask the children what they might be doing at that time. Repeat for different times.

Week 13

A bag of toys
Easy

• *Counting up to 10 objects*
• *Estimating quantities*
Number cards (1 to 10), small soft toys, a feely bag

Give each child three number cards. Place a number of small soft toys in a feely bag. Show the bag to the children and ask them to estimate how many toys it contains. Tip out the toys and count them. If a child has that number on one of their cards, they turn it over. The first child to turn over all of their cards is the winner.

Action track
Medium

• *Counting movements*
A number track (1 to 20), a coin, counters, interlocking cubes

The children place their counters on number 1 on the track. In turn, they spin a coin and move their counter accordingly: heads move forwards two spaces, tails move forwards one space. As a child lands on a space, the other children choose an action for the child to do that number of times. If the child does the action the correct number of times, they take a cube. The children continue until someone reaches number 20. The winner is the child with the most cubes.

What noises!
Hard

• *Counting sounds*
A 4 x 5 grid, counters, a coin, interlocking cubes

Number the grid from 1 to 20. Ask the children to put their counters on number 1. They take turns to spin a coin and move their counter accordingly: tails move left or right, heads move up or down. As they land on a square, the children make a noise that number of times, e.g. 15 moos. If they make the correct number of noises, they collect a cube. After six turns each, the winner is the child with the most cubes.

Term 2

Week 1

What's next?
Easy

• *Saying the next number to any given number*

A number track (1 to 12), a coin, counters

Ask the children to place their counters on number 1. In turn, they spin a coin and move their counter accordingly: heads move forwards two spaces, tails move forwards one space. The children say the number they land on and then say the next number. If they are correct, they move to the next space. If not, they move back three spaces (or to 1). The first to reach 12 is the winner.

Covered numbers
Medium

• *Saying the next number to any given number*

A number track (1 to 20), interlocking cubes (in different colours)

Divide the children into small groups and give each child some cubes in a different colour. In turn, the children say a number on the line, cover the next number with a cube and say that number. If they are correct, they leave the cube where it is; otherwise, they remove it. The children continue until all the numbers are covered with a cube. *Who has covered the most numbers?* Ask them to remove their cubes, build a tower with them and count them to find out who placed the most on the track.

Put it down!
Hard

• *Saying the next number to any given number*

Number cards (1 to 21)

Shuffle the cards and place the number 10 card face up on the table. Deal out the rest of the cards so that each child has five. In turn, the children place one of their cards on the table, but only if a number next to one of theirs has already been placed. So the first player can put down either number 9 or 11. The winner is the first to place all of their cards on the table.

Week 2

Count the jigsaw
Easy

• *Counting up to 15 objects*

A jigsaw

Tip out the pieces of a jigsaw. Help the children to estimate the number of pieces. Then count the pieces together, grouping them in fives. *Was the estimate close to the actual number?* Make up the jigsaw together and count the pieces again.

The tallest tower
Medium

• *Starting to record numbers to mark the number in a set*

Number cards (1 to 20), interlocking cubes

Shuffle the cards and place them face down in a pile. The children each take a card. *Who has the largest number?* They count out cubes to match their card number and make a tower with them. *Who has made the tallest tower?* That child writes their number on the board. The children replace their cards at the bottom of the pile and continue until one of them has written five numbers.

How many in a handful?
Hard

• *Counting up to 20 objects*
• *Starting to record numbers to mark the number in a set*

Number cards (1 to 20), beads, a number track (1 to 20)

Ask each child to take a handful of beads and estimate the number. They take a number card to match their estimate. Helping each other, the children count each handful of beads, grouping the beads in fives. They then write down the total of their own handful. Using a number track, help them to compare their counts with their estimates. How close were they?

Week 3

Place it
Easy

• *Using the language of position*

Toy animals, a box

Invite a child to take an animal and say a position. *Above.* Let another child place that animal in that position relative to the box. Continue until all the animals have been placed. Then ask a child to look at an animal and say a position. *Under the box.* The other children have to guess which animal is being referred to. Repeat until all the animals have been selected.

Around the house
Medium

• *Placing objects in given positions*

A large picture of a house or tent, adhesive cartoon stickers, position cards ('above', 'beneath', 'under', 'inside', 'outside', 'next to')

Display the picture and ask the children, in turn, to take one of the position cards. Read the card and invite the children to take a cartoon sticker and stick it in that position on the house or tent. Continue until all the stickers have been positioned, reusing the position cards if necessary.

Grid positions
Hard

• *Using the language of position*
A 3 x 5 grid, counters (in three different colours)

Place the counters on the grid. Ask individual children to place new counters on the grid, according to your instructions. *Put a blue counter below the yellow counter.* Use specific positional language and encourage the children to repeat the words as they place the counters.

Week 4

Add 1 more
Easy

• *Adding 1 to a number up to 10*
A number track (1 to 10), building bricks

Ask each child to choose a number on the track and to collect that number of bricks. They then say how many bricks they will have if they take another one. If they are correct, they keep the bricks. If not, they put the bricks back. Let the children have six turns each and then make a model with their bricks.

Up the ladder
Medium

• *Adding 2 to a number up to 10*
A long sheet of paper, a toy cat

Draw a ladder with ten numbered rungs on the paper. Place the cat on the bottom rung. *Where will the cat be if we move him up two rungs?* Let the children tell you the correct answer and write the matching number sentence, i.e. 1 + 2 = 3. Invite one of the children to move the cat to see if he reaches the predicted rung. Repeat several times, positioning the cat on different rungs.

Adding bricks
Hard

• *Adding 2 to a number up to 20*
A number track (1 to 20), a coin, counters, building bricks

Give each child a counter and let them place them on number 1. In turn, the children spin a coin and move their counter accordingly: heads move forwards three spaces, tails move forwards two spaces. The children look at the number they land on and take that number of bricks, plus 2, e.g. they land on 3 and take five bricks. If they are correct, they keep the bricks. If not, they replace them. Continue until all the children reach the end of the track. *Who has the most bricks?*

Week 5

Six egg men
Easy

• *Understanding addition as a combination of two sets*
A half-dozen egg box, six egg men

Paint faces on hard-boiled eggs to make 'egg men'. Put an egg man in each section of the egg box. *How many egg men are out of the box? None.* Write the number sentence, 6 + 0 = 6. Take out one egg man from the box and tell the children that he has gone shopping. *How many men are still at home? How many men have gone out?* Write the corresponding number sentence, 5 + 1 = 6. Cover the other number sentences (4 + 2 = 6, 3 + 3 = 6, ...) in the same way.

Sharing coins
Medium

• *Understanding addition as a combination of two sets*
Purses, 1p coins

Divide the children into pairs. Give each pair a purse and eight coins. Ask them to share the coins equally between the two purses. *How many coins are in each purse?* Write the number sentence, 4 + 4 = 8. Ask one child in each pair to give a coin to the other child. *How much is in each purse now?* Write the number sentence, 5 + 3 = 8. Continue to cover the other two number sentences in the same way.

Purses of coins
Hard

• *Understanding addition as a combination of two sets*
Purses, 1p coins

In pairs, ask the children to find out all the possible ways of sharing 10p between two purses. When they think they have found them all, help them to write the number sentence for each possibility. Ask the children to repeat the investigation, this time using 2p and 5p coins as well.

Week 6

Snake lengths
Easy

• *Beginning to measure length using a non-standard unit*
Paper snakes of different lengths, crayons

Give each child a paper snake and a supply of crayons. Encourage the children to lay the crayons from end to end along the length of the snake. *How many crayons long is your snake?* Compare the numbers of crayons used to measure the snakes. *Who has the longest snake?*

Fish lengths
Medium

• *Beginning to measure length using a non-standard unit*
• *Comparing the lengths of objects*
Paper fish of different lengths, interlocking cubes, a large sheet of paper, crayons, glue

Let each child choose a paper fish and measure its length using interlocking cubes. *How many cubes long is your fish? Who has the longest fish?* Invite the children to decorate the sheet of paper to look like the sea. Let the children glue the fish to the paper in order of length and write next to them the length, in cubes, of each fish.

Straw heights
Hard

• *Beginning to measure length using a non-standard unit*
• *Comparing the lengths of objects*
Several straws, two large books

In turn, ask the children to lie down on the floor. Make sure that they are as straight as possible and then place one book at the top of their head and one below their feet. Ask the child to stand up carefully, without disturbing the books, and measure the space between the two books with straws. Record the height in straws of each child. *How many straws tall is Harriet? Who is the tallest child? Who is the shortest child?*

Week 7

Heavy boxes
Easy

• *Comparing heavy and light objects*

Three identical boxes, sand, dried beans, cotton wool, balance scales

Fill one box with sand, one with dried beans and one with cotton wool. Show the children the boxes and their contents, then ask them to guess which is the heaviest. In turn, balance the boxes on the scales against one of the other boxes, explaining that the heaviest side will go down. Were the children's guesses correct? Repeat to find out which is the lightest box.

Shoe weights
Medium

• *Comparing heavy and light objects*

Children's shoes, balance scales

Ask each child to take off one of their shoes. Look at the shoes and ask the children to guess which is the heaviest and which is the lightest. Use the scales to find out by balancing the shoes against each other. Were the children's guesses correct?

Heavy tins
Hard

• *Comparing heavy and light objects*

Four different types of tins (e.g. beans, sweets, fish), balance scales

Show the children the four tins and ask them which one they think is the heaviest and which is the lightest. Help the children to use the scales to find out by balancing each tin against each other. Were the children's guesses correct?

Week 8

Tracking numbers
Easy

• *Comparing two or three numbers*

A number track (1 to 20), a coin, counters, interlocking cubes

The children place their counters on number 1. In turn, they spin a coin and move their counter along the number track accordingly: heads move forwards three spaces, tails move forwards two spaces. After each turn, the children look at the number they are on, take the same number of cubes and build a tower with them. *Who is on the largest number? Who is furthest along the track?* The child on the largest number keeps a cube and the rest are replaced. When the children reach the end of the track, the child with the most cubes is the winner.

Mine's larger
Medium

• *Comparing two or three numbers*

Number cards (1 to 20), interlocking cubes

Shuffle the cards and place them face down in a pile. In turn, the children each take a card. They compare their numbers. The child with the largest number takes a cube. The children continue until all the cards have been taken. The child with the most cubes is the winner.

Making tracks
Hard

• *Ordering numbers to 30*

Number cards (1 to 30), a number track (1 to 30)

Give each child six number cards and ask them to line them up in order from smallest to largest. Let the children compare the order of their numbers with those on a number track. Did they put their cards in the correct order? Extend to use number cards up to 50.

Week 9

Losing beads
Easy

• *Counting backwards from 12*

Number cards (1 to 12), beads, laces

Shuffle the cards and place them face up at random. Give each child a lace with a knot at one end and ask them to thread twelve beads on it. Invite a child to find the number 12 card and position it away from the others. Ask all the children to remove a bead from their lace and to count the remaining beads. *How many beads are on your lace? Can you find the matching number card?* Let a child place the 11 card next to the 12 card. Continue until all twelve cards have been placed in a row and the children have removed all the beads from their lace.

Losing money
Medium

• *Counting backwards from 20*

A number track (1 to 20), counters, 1p coins

Ask the children to place their counters on 20 on the number track and to take twenty 1p coins each. In turn, they spin a coin and move their counter accordingly: heads move backwards two spaces, tails move backwards one space. They remove either one or two coins from their pile, according to how many spaces they have moved, and say how many coins they have left. The children continue until they reach number 1.

A penny a card
Hard

• *Counting backwards from 20*
Number cards (1 to 20), 1p coins
Shuffle the cards and place them face down in a pile. In turn, the children take a card, count backwards to 1 from that number. If they are correct, they take a 1p coin. The children continue until all the cards have been taken. The winner is the child with the most money.

Week 10

Cubes or not
Easy

• *Recognising and naming a cube*
A variety of 3-d shapes including cubes, labels ('cubes', 'not cubes')
Read the labels to the children and place them apart on a table. Ask the children to sort the 3-d shapes into two sets and place them next to the correct labels.

Repeat the pattern
Medium

• *Sorting 3-d shapes*
3-d shapes (large and small cubes, cuboids, cones)
Place some shapes in a row to make a pattern. Ask the children to look closely at the pattern and then copy it. Encourage them to name the shapes as they place them. How many times can they repeat the pattern?

Decorate a cuboid
Hard

• *Recognising and naming a cuboid*
Nets of cuboids, sticky tape, coloured pencils, adhesive shapes
Give each child a net of a cuboid and ask them to decorate the outside faces. Help them to fold along the edges of the cuboid and put it together. Can they name the shape? *How many faces does the cuboid have? What shape are the faces?*

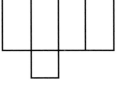

Week 11

Coins on the track
Easy

• *Recognising coins*
A number track (1 to 20), coins (1p, 2p, 5p, 10p, 20p)
In turn, ask the children to take a coin and place it on the matching number on the line. Discuss what you could buy with each coin.

At the greengrocer's
Medium

• *Recognising coins*
Different fruits and vegetables, price labels, coins (2p, 5p, 10p)

Price the fruit and vegetables, each at either 2p, 5p or 10p. In turn, each child picks an item and chooses the correct coin to pay for it. Ask the children questions about the shape and colour of the coins.

Coin rubbings
Hard

• *Recognising coins*
Coins (all denominations), wax crayons

Ask the children to choose a coin. Show them how to make a coin rubbing and then let them make their own. Encourage them to make a rubbing of each coin. As they work, talk with them about the shapes and colours of the coins. Can they write the value of each coin next to its rubbing?

Week 12

Daily tools
Easy

• *Recognising the hours on an analogue clock*
Pictures of household items, a sheet showing clock faces with times on the hour, glue

Show the children a variety of pictures of household objects that we use at certain times of the day, e.g. a toothbrush, a knife and fork, a bed. Ask the children to select some of the pictures and stick them next to the clock which shows an approximate time when that object might be used. E.g. a picture of a bed could be stuck next to 7 o'clock.

Daily routines
Medium

• *Recognising the hours on an analogue clock*
An analogue clock with movable hands

Set the hands of the clock on an hour. *What time is this? Can you tell me something that you usually do at this time of day?* Repeat several times, including the same hours in the morning and at night.

It takes an hour
Hard

• *Reading and setting the time to the hour on an analogue clock*
A clock stamp

Give each child a piece of paper with two clock stamps on it. Say a time, e.g. *Two o'clock*. Help the children to mark the hour on one clock stamp. Discuss what time is one hour later. *Three o'clock*. The children mark this time on the other clock stamp. Encourage the children to draw a picture of what might take them an hour to do.

Week 13

Move that number
Easy

- *Counting movements*

A number track (1 to 10), counters, a coin, interlocking cubes

Ask the children to place their counters on 1 on the number track. In turn, the children spin a coin and move their counter along the track accordingly: heads move two spaces, tails move one space. When they have moved their counter, the other children choose an action, such as clap, jump or hop. The child who moved the counter performs the action the same number of times as the space they are on. If they count correctly, they take a cube. Continue until one child reaches number 10. The winner is the child with the most cubes.

Number noises
Medium

- *Counting sounds*
- *Counting up to 30*

A 5 x 6 grid, counters, a coin, interlocking cubes

Number the grid from 1 to 30. Ask the children to put their counters on number 1. In turn, the children spin a coin and move their counter on the grid accordingly: tails move left or right, heads move up or down. When they land on a square, the child chooses and makes a noise the same number of times as the square they are on. If they count correctly, they take a cube. When one child lands on number 30 the children count their cubes. The winner is the child with the most cubes.

Beads in a mug
Hard

- *Estimating quantities*
- *Counting up to 50 objects*

A mug, beads

Fill a mug with beads and ask each child to estimate the number of beads. Write down the children's estimates. Tip out the beads and count them together, first by grouping them in twos and then in tens. Compare the actual total with the children's estimates. *Whose estimate is the closest?*

Term 3

Week 1

Moving on
Easy

• *Saying the next number to any given number*
A number track (1 to 12), a coin, a counters

Ask the children to place their counters on 1 on the number track. In turn, the children spin a coin and move their counter accordingly: heads move two spaces, tails move one space. The children say the number they land on and then say the next number. If they are correct, they move to that number. If not, they move back three spaces (or back to 1). The first child to reach number 12 is the winner.

Covering numbers
Medium

• *Saying the next number to any given number*
A number track (1 to 20), different-coloured interlocking cubes

In turn, the children choose a number on the track and say it. They then cover the next number with a cube and say the number. If they are correct, they leave the cube on the line, otherwise they remove it. The children continue until all the numbers are covered. The winner is the child with the most cubes on the line.

A hundred cards
Hard

• *Counting to 100*
Number cards (1 to 100)

Shuffle the cards and place them face down in a pile. The children take turns to pick a card and place it so that, eventually, all the cards are in order from 1 to 100.

Week 2

The tallest tower
Easy

• *Recording numbers to mark the number in a set*
Number cards (1 to 20), interlocking cubes

Shuffle the cards and place them face down in a pile. In turn, each child takes a card. *Who has the largest number?* The children count out the number of cubes to match their card number and make a tower with them. The child who has made the tallest tower writes down the number of their cubes. The cards are replaced at the bottom of the pile and the children continue until one of them has written five numbers.

Counting pages
Medium

• *Counting up to 20 objects*
A small story book, sugar paper, coloured pencils, crayons

Look at the story book together and count the number of pages devoted to the story. Help the children to make their own books and to illustrate them. *How many pages does your book have?*

Counting clips
Hard

• *Counting up to 50 objects*
• *Counting in twos and tens*
A box of paperclips or similar small objects

Tip out the paperclips and ask the children to guess how many there are. Write down their estimates. *What is the best way to count the paperclips? Shall we count them in twos or tens?* Count them together and find out whose estimate was the closest.

Week 3

Move it this way
Easy

- *Beginning to use the language of direction*

A large 4 x 4 grid, a soft toy, a small object

Put the toy somewhere on the grid. Ask one child to give directions and another child to move the toy accordingly. *Move it two spaces to the right and then two spaces forwards.* Repeat with other children. Then place a small object on one of the spaces and ask one of the children to direct the toy to it, using the correct language as they do so. (They do not need to go the shortest route.) *Move three spaces forwards, two spaces right and three spaces backwards.* Repeat several times.

Stick it there
Medium

- *Moving in given directions in relation to a starting point*

A 4 x 4 grid, adhesive cartoon characters

Ask a child to stick a character in one of the central spaces on the grid. That child then instructs another child to stick another character somewhere else on the grid, using the correct language. *Move up two spaces and left one space.* Continue until each space on the grid contains a character.

Grid counters
Hard

- *Moving in given directions in relation to a starting point*

A 5 x 5 grid, different-coloured counters

Place three different-coloured counters on the grid. Give each child a counter and give them, in turn, an instruction to place it in relation to counters already on the grid. *Starting at the red counter, move two spaces down and three spaces along to the right.* Continue until each child has placed their counter.

Week 4

And 3 more makes ...
Easy

- *Adding by counting on*

A number track (1 to 20), building bricks

Encourage each child to choose a number on the track and match it with the same number of bricks. In turn, the children then say how many bricks they will have if they take 3 more. If they are correct, they keep the bricks. If not, they put them back. Continue until the children have had six turns each. The children then build a model with their bricks.

Cat up a ladder
Medium

- *Adding by counting on*
- *Subtracting by counting back*

A long sheet of paper, a toy cat, interlocking cubes

Draw a ladder with 20 numbered rungs on the paper. Place a toy cat on the bottom rung. *Where will the cat be if we move him up three rungs?* Ask one of the children to move the cat to see if their predictions were correct. Write the number sentence on the board. Give the children who were correct a cube. Repeat, starting on different rungs. Then repeat the activity, this time moving the cat back 3 rungs. *Who has collected the most cubes?*

**Forwards and
backwards**
Hard

- *Adding by counting on*
- *Subtracting by counting back*

A number track (1 to 20), a coin, counters

Ask the children to place their counters on number 10. In turn, the children spin a coin and move their counter accordingly: heads move forwards three spaces, tails move backwards two spaces. Before they move their counter, the children must say where their counter will land. The first child to reach either end of the number track with their counter wins.

Week 5

Ladybird spots
Easy

- *Understanding addition as the combination of two sets*

A large sheet of paper, counters, a red crayon

Draw a ladybird on the sheet of paper. Put three counters on each wing and explain that they represent the ladybird's spots. Write the matching number sentence, e.g. 3 + 3 = 6, and read it together. Move one counter to the other wing and write the corresponding sentence. Read it together. Continue until all the counters are on one wing.

Sharing it out
Medium

- *Understanding addition as the partitioning of a set*

Purses, 1p coins

Divide the children into pairs. Give each pair a purse and ten coins. Ask them to share the coins equally between the two purses. *How many coins are in each purse?* Write the number sentence to match. Ask the children to find different ways to share the coins. *How much is in each purse now?* Write the number sentences to match. *How many ways can we share coins?* Repeat with a different number of coins.

Towers of 10
Hard

- *Understanding addition as the partitioning of a set*

Building bricks in two different colours

Ask each child to build towers of ten bricks using two different colours. Encourage them to build as many different towers as they can. When they have finished, help them to write the matching number sentence for each tower. *Can they read each sentence?* Repeat for different-sized towers.

Week 6

Paper fish
Easy

• *Measuring a length using a non-standard unit*
Paper fish in different lengths, interlocking cubes, crayons

Give each child a paper fish and some cubes. Let the children look at each other's fish and compare their lengths. *Whose fish is the longest/shortest?* Show them how to measure their fish by linking the cubes together and laying them along its length. *Whose fish needs the most/fewest cubes?* Compare the lengths of the cube links. *Did the child with the longest fish make the longest cube link?* Give the children crayons to measure the lengths of the fish in the same way. *Who will need the most crayons?*

How tall are you?
Medium

• *Measuring a height using a non-standard unit*
Crayons

In pairs, encourage the children to measure each other's height using crayons. Explain that one of them should lie down while the other places crayons, end to end, along the side of the child, from their feet to their head. When they have done this, record the height of the child in crayons and let the children repeat the activity, swapping roles. *How many crayons tall is the tallest child?*

Hand spans
Hard

• *Measuring a length using a non-standard unit*
Interlocking cubes

In turn, ask each child to spread out their hand on a piece of paper. Mark where the tip of their thumb and their little finger reach. Encourage the children to measure between the two points with interlocking cubes. *Who has the longest/shortest hand span? How many cubes long is Kavita's hand span?*

Week 7

Measuring bottles
Easy

• *Comparing capacity*
Three different-shaped bottles, water, a water tray

Show the children two different-shaped bottles. *Which of these bottles holds most water?* Fill one of them with water and then pour the water into the other bottle. Were the children correct? Show the children a third bottle. *Which one of the three bottles holds most water?* Fill one of them with water and pour the water into the other two bottles, one at a time. Let the children order the bottles according to their capacity.

Eggcupfuls
Medium

• *Comparing the capacity of two containers*
An eggcup, a small plastic bottle, water, a water tray

Divide the children into pairs and give each pair an eggcup and a small plastic bottle. *How many eggcupfuls of water do you think will fit into your bottle?* Make a note of the children's estimates and then ask them to find the answer by filling the bottle with water and repeatedly pouring it out into the eggcup. They should count each eggcup of water and then compare the total number with their estimate. *How close were your estimates?*

A box of lentils
Hard

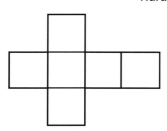

• *Finding a capacity using a non-standard unit*
A net of a cube, sticky tape, lentils, a spoon, newspaper

Give each child a net of a cube and help them to make it into a box, leaving one side open. *How many spoonfuls of lentils do you think your box will hold?* Write down the children's estimates and invite them to find out the answer. Over a sheet of newspaper, let each child spoon the lentils into their box, counting the spoonfuls one at a time. How close were their estimates to the actual number?

Week 8

Between numbers
Easy

• *Recognising numbers between given numbers*
A number track (1 to 20), red and blue counters, a coin

Divide the children into pairs and give each child two counters in the same colour to place on number 1. In turn, the children spin a coin and move one of their counters accordingly: heads move forwards three spaces, tails move forwards two spaces. When each child has moved their first counter, tell them to pause and look at where their counters are. *Which numbers are between the two numbers your counters are on?* The children should say the numbers, then move their second counter onto the same number as the first. They continue until they both reach the end of the track.

Bigger or smaller?
Medium

• *Comparing two numbers*
Number cards (1 to 10)

Ask the children to sit in pairs. Shuffle the cards and give one to each child. Encourage the children to say the number on their card and ask the child with the smaller number in each pair to hold up their card. Repeat with the larger number.

What comes in between?
Hard

• *Recognising numbers between given numbers*
Number cards (1 to 20), a number track (1 to 20), interlocking cubes

Give each group of four children a set of cards. Shuffle the cards and place them face down in a pile. Turn over the top card and leave it face up on the table. Invite each child to take a card. In turn, they each say the numbers that come between their card and the one face up, using a number track to help them, if necessary. If they are correct, they take a cube for each in-between number they said. The children continue until all the cards have been taken. *Who has collected the most cubes?*

Week 9

How many are left?
Easy

• *Removing a small number of objects from a larger number*
Number cards (4 to 10), interlocking cubes

Encourage the children to line up the number cards in order. Let them place one cube on each number up to 10. The children take turns to take away three cubes from the line. Before they remove them, they must say how many cubes will be left on the line. If they are correct, they keep the cubes.

Collecting coins
Medium

• *Removing a small number of objects from a larger number*
A number track (4 to 20), 1p coins

Place a coin on each number on the track. The children take turns to remove three coins. Before they do, they must say how many coins will be left on the track. If they are correct, they keep the coins. When all the coins have been removed, who has collected the most?

Counting back 3
Hard

• *Counting back to find a remainder*
Number cards (4 to 25), 1p coins

Shuffle the cards and place them face down in a pile. The children take turns to take a card and count back 3 from that number. If they are correct, they take a 1p coin. They continue until all the cards have been taken. *Who has collected the most coins?*

Week 10

Sort them out
Easy

• *Sorting 3-d shapes*
• *Recognising cubes and cuboids*
A variety of 3-d shapes (including cubes and cuboids), labels ('cubes', 'cuboids', 'other shapes')

Read the labels to the children and ensure that they understand which is which. Place the labels on a table and ask the children to sort the 3-d shapes and place them next to the correct label.

A 3-d pattern
Medium

• *Sorting 3-d shapes*

3-d shapes (cubes, cuboids, pyramids, cones)

Place one each of the four shapes in a row to make a pattern. Ask the children to use the 3-d shapes to copy the pattern and to say the name of each shape as they position it. *How many times can you repeat the same pattern?* Encourage them to talk about the properties of the shapes, e.g. the shape of the faces, flat or curved faces, ...

Making shapes
Hard

• *Recognising and naming cubes and cuboids*

Nets of cubes and cuboids, sticky tape, coloured pencils, adhesive shapes

Give each child a net of a cube or cuboid and ask them to decorate the outside faces. Help them to fold along the edges to put it together. *What is the name of this shape? How many faces does it have? What shape are the faces?*

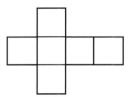 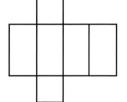

Week 11

The same value
Easy

• *Recognising coins*
• *Matching coins with the same value*

Coins (all denominations), biscuits

Show the children the coins and ask a child to take one of them. *Which coin have you chosen?* Help another child to find other coins which have the same total value as the first coin. If they choose the correct coins, let them buy a biscuit with their coins. Repeat with different coins.

Food shopping
Medium

• *Recognising coins*
• *Matching coins with the same value*

Different food items, price labels, coins (1p, 2p, 5p, 10p)

Price food items, all at either 2p, 5p or 10p. In turn, each child chooses an item and uses two or more coins to pay for it. Encourage the shopper to count out the coins to make the appropriate value. The shopkeeper should check the total each time.

Clubbing together
Hard

- *Recognising coins*

Coins (1p, 2p, 5p, 10p, 20p)

Give each child a coin and ask them to find a partner. Each pair then adds their coins together to find out how much they have between them. Help them to write the number sentence, e.g. 5p + 2p = 7p. Repeat the activity, giving different coins to each child and finding different partners.

Week 12

Special days
Easy

- *Recognising the days of the week*

Large sheets of paper

Help the children to create posters, one for weekdays and one for weekends. Encourage them to draw or write something special that is associated with weekdays, e.g. a lunchbox, and with weekends, e.g. a bicycle.

My own calendar
Medium

- *Recognising the days of the week*
- *Ordering days of the week*

Large sheets of paper

Help each child to create their own calendar for a week. Say the days of the week together and help them to write the name of each day on their calendar. Under each day, encourage the children to draw or write something that is special for that day, e.g. a football under 'Wednesday', an ice-cream under 'Saturday', and so on.

Using calendars
Hard

- *Beginning to understand today, tomorrow and yesterday*

A current calendar

Look together at the current month on a calendar. Discuss how the days are marked. *Which day of the week is it today? Can you find today's date on the calendar? What will the date be tomorrow? What was the date yesterday?* Discuss some forthcoming events with the children. If there is room, write or draw a symbol for some of them on the calendar. *On which days should we mark the calendar?*

Week 13

Covering numbers
Easy

- *Counting to 100*
- *Beginning to count in tens*

A number track (1 to 20), counters, 10p coins

In turn, the children choose a number and place a counter on it. They then say the number before and the number after. If they are correct, they take a 10p coin. The children continue until all the numbers on the track are covered with a counter. Ask the children to count how much money they have. The winner is the child with the most money.

Grid movements
Medium

• *Recognising larger numbers*
• *Beginning to count in tens*
A 6 x 6 grid, counters, 10p coins

Number the grid from 1 to 36. Give each child a counter and ask them to place them on number 1 on the grid. In turn, the children spin a coin and move their counter accordingly: heads move up or down, tails move left or right. The children must say the number they land on and the number which is 1 more. If they are correct, they take a 10p coin. The children continue until they each have had six turns. Ask the children to count how much money they have. The winner is the child with the most money.

Estimating leaves
Hard

• *Counting to 100*
• *Beginning to count in tens*
A branch or twig with leaves on

Show the children the branch or twig. Ask them to estimate the number of leaves it has. Write down the children's names and their estimates. Let the children help you to pull off the leaves then count them, grouping them in twos and then in tens. Compare the actual number of leaves with the children's estimates. *Who had the closest estimate?*

Counting

Counting to 20

Drum the number

- *Counting to 20*
- *Counting sounds*

Number cards (1 to 20), a drum and beater

Give out a number card at random to each child. Beat the drum up to 20 times. Ask the children to secretly count the beats. Encourage the child holding the card that matches the number of beats to hold it up and say the number. Extend the activity by turning your back on the children as you beat the drum so that they have to count the sound of the beats. This is a much more difficult task. Alternatively, give each child number cards 1 to 6. Beat the drum with your back to the children. Ask the children to count the beats and turn the matching number card over.

Bouncing numbers

- *Counting to 20*
- *Counting movements*

Large number cards (1 to 20), a ball

Spread out the number cards at random on the floor. Ask the children to watch while you bounce the ball a number of times. Ask the children to count the bounces and then run to stand by the appropriate number card. Check that they are correct then all jump up and down that number of times. Repeat several times. Extend the activity by asking the children to count the bounces and stand by the number card that is one more or one less than that number of bounces.

Twenty bricks high

• *Counting to 20*

Two sets of number cards (1 to 20) in different colours, building bricks

Divide the children into two teams. Shuffle the cards separately and place the two sets face down between the children. Select a child from each team to turn over a card from their pile. The teams build a tower of bricks to match the number on their card. Repeat until one team turns over the 20 card and builds a tower of 20 bricks. *Who has the most bricks in total?*

Open wide!

• *Counting movements*

Two sets of number cards (1 to 20), a hand puppet

Shuffle the number cards and give three to each child. (You may need to check that the children have been given appropriate numbers.) Ask them to turn the cards over.

Invite the children to watch and count as you operate the puppet and open its mouth up to 20 times. *How many times did the puppet open its mouth?* If a child has that number card they hold it up and say the number. Repeat with other numbers.

How many in the packet?

• *Counting to 20*
• *Counting in twos*

A packet of sweets or biscuits, a large sheet of paper

Show the children the packet of sweets or biscuits and ask them to estimate how many sweets or biscuits it contains. Help the children to write their estimates on the board. Empty the packet onto a sheet of paper and count the items, arranging them in twos as you count. Write the total number on the board and compare it with the children's estimates. *Whose estimate is close to the actual number? Are there enough sweets/biscuits for everyone to have one? How do you know?*

Counting up to 20 objects

Pennies in a purse

• *Counting up to 20 objects*

A purse containing a variety of coins including several 1p coins, Post-it notes, a number track (1 to 20)

Tip out the contents of the purse. *Are they all 1p coins? If we want to count just the 1p coins, what do we need to do first?* Select a child to separate the 1p coins from the other coins. *About how many coins do you think there are? What must we do to find out?* Ask the children to estimate the number of coins. Help them to write their name and the number of their estimate on a Post-it note. Choose a child to count out the 1p coins, encouraging the other children to join in with the count. *How many 1p coins are there? Who can find the number on the number track? Whose estimate is the nearest?* Count the 1p coins again by grouping them in twos.

Team work

• *Counting up to 20 objects*

Number cards (1 to 20), a plastic plate, counters or interlocking cubes

Give each pair of children a plate. Ask each pair to count out twenty counters or cubes. Shuffle the cards and place them face down in a pile. Invite a child to turn over the top card and read it out. *How quickly can you count that number of counters or cubes onto the plate?* Explain that they should put up their hands to show that they have finished. Together, count out the objects to check that they are correct. Repeat several times. (This activity is more difficult than it appears because the children in each pair need to work co-operatively.)

Take a handful

• *Counting up to 20 objects*

A number track (1 to 20), interlocking cubes or counters

Invite pairs of children to take a handful of cubes or counters and to count how many they have, making a tower of cubes if necessary. Each pair then says their total and points to the correct number on the number track. If necessary, let the children count up the number track to find their number.

Counting forwards and backwards

Snaking around

- *Counting forwards and backwards to and from 10*

Large number cards (1 to 10), chalk

On the playground, draw a large number snake with ten segments, numbered 1 to 10. In turn, give each child a card and invite them to stand in the appropriate segment. The rest of the children should help the child to jump forwards to 10 or backwards to 1, by calling out the numbers in sequence. Repeat several times.

Ten toys in our row

- *Counting backwards from 10*
- *Recgonising numbers to 10*

Ten soft toys numbered 1 to 10, a box

Lay the toys on the floor and ask the children to arrange them in the correct order. Together, count along the line to check. Encourage the children to tidy the toys into the box singing this song to the tune of 'Ten green bottles'.

Ten cuddly toys standing in our row,
Ten cuddly toys standing in our row,
If one cuddly toy should fall into the box,
There'll be nine cuddly toys standing in our row.

Estimating

Money box

- *Estimating quantities*
- *Counting in twos*

Number cards (1 to 30), 1p coins, Post-it notes

Lay out the number cards in order and place the 1p coins on the floor. *About how many 1p coins are there?* Invite a child to estimate the number, write their name on a Post-it note and put the note on the estimated number card. Repeat with two or three other children. Count out the coins in twos. *How many coins are there?* Place a Post-it note on the correct number. Look at the estimates together. *Who had the nearest guess?*

What's your guess?

- *Estimating quantities*

Teddy counters, pegs, pieces of card, felt-tipped pens

Invite two children each to take a handful of teddy counters and put them together in a pile. *About how many teddies are in the pile?* Help the children to write their estimates. Encourage them to count out the teddies in twos. *How many do we have? Who had the closest guess?* Write the actual number on a card and place it on the pile. Then invite two children each to take a handful of pegs and place them in a pile. *Do you think we have more or fewer pegs than teddies in this pile? About how many pegs do you think there are?* Repeat, recording the estimates and counting the pegs.

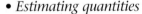

Across the playground

- *Estimating quantities*

Ask the children to estimate how many steps you will need to take across the playground. Write down some of the estimates with the children's names. Encourage the children to stand in a straight line at one side of the playground. Step and count together to the other side. *How many steps did we take? Did we all take the same number of steps?* Find out whose estimate was the closest to the actual number. Ask the children if they think the number of steps will be the same if they bounce or hop across the playground. Try out the actions to see if the children's guesses were correct.

About how many?

- *Estimating quantities*
- *Recording numbers to mark the number in a set*

Number cards (1 to 20), a bag of potatoes, Post-it notes

Hold up the bag of potatoes. *About how many potatoes do you think are in this bag? Can you write the number that you think it could be?* Help each child to write their estimate on a Post-it note. *How will we find out how many there are?* Select a child to count the potatoes, laying them in a row as they are counted. Choose another child to number the potatoes with a card. *How many potatoes are there? Can you read your estimated numbers? Who has the closest estimate?* The children stick their Post-it notes in order below the number card so that they can see more easily whose estimate is the closest.

Counting in tens

Counting conkers

- *Counting to 100*
- *Counting in tens*

A large bag of conkers, ten containers (labelled 10, 20, 30 ... 100)

Hold up the bag of conkers and tell the children that you are going to count them together. Tip out the conkers and invite a child to count ten of them. Encourage the other children to help with the counting. Ask a second child to count the next group from 11 to 20. Continue until all the conkers have been counted. Ask the children to put the conkers into the containers in groups of ten and to count them again in tens. *How many conkers are there altogether?*

How many sweets?

• Counting to 100
• Counting in tens

A bag of sweets, a number grid (1 to 100)

Hold up the bag of sweets. *How many sweets do you think are in this bag?* Help the children to write their names and estimates on the board. Refer them to the number grid if necessary. Tip out the sweets and select a child to count out ten, put them on a piece of paper and write '10'. Choose another child to count sweets from 11 to 20 in the same way. Encourage all the children to help with the counting. Continue counting in groups of 10 until all the sweets have been counted. Together, count the sweets in tens, pointing to the sweets and the written numbers as you count. *Can anyone see the numbers we have counted on the number grid? Where are they on the grid?* Count in tens down the grid while a child counts the sweets in tens.

Reading and writing numbers

Recognising numerals

Car numbers

• *Recognising numbers up to 9*
• *Writing numerals to 9*
Number cards (1 to 9)
Take the children to look at some cars parked outside. Choose a car and look at the number plate. Identify the three numbers and select a child to match the car numbers with the number cards. Read the numbers together. Ask another child to write the three numbers. Repeat with other car numbers.

Ten green bottles

• *Recognising numbers to 10*
• *Counting backwards from 10*
Ten green paper bottles numbered 1 to 10
Ask the children to help you attach paper bottles to the wall with their numbers showing in the correct order. Sing 'Ten green bottles' together as the children count down the bottles. Choose a child to remove a bottle at the end of each verse and count down the remaining number of bottles.

Put them in order

• *Recognising numbers to 20*
• *Counting to 20*
Number cards (1 to 20)
Place the number 10 card on the table and deal out the others between the children. The children take turns to lay out cards in order. They can only lay down a card that is one more or one less than a card that is already on the table. I.e. 9 or 11 to start. Continue until the cards are all positioned. Ask the children to close their eyes as you turn over a card. *Which card is hiding? How do you know? Rosie, can you turn the card over so that we can check?* Ask the children to stand up and jump that number of times, counting each jump.

Musical numbers

- *Recognising numbers to 20*
- *Counting to 20*

Instruments (such as wooden blocks or triangles), number cards (1 to 20), a number track (1 to 20)

Divide the children into pairs and give each pair an instrument. Shuffle the cards and place them face down in a pile. Select a child to turn over the top card. *What is the number?* The children may need to count along the number track to identify it. Encourage them to count up to that number. As they do so, those with the instruments play them and the other children clap that many times. Help the children to keep in time. Repeat, with the children swapping roles.

Between two bears

- *Recognising a set of numbers more or less than a given number*
- *Recognising numbers in between given numbers*

Two teddy bears, number cards (1 to 10), Blu-tack

Shuffle the number cards and place them face down in a pile. Ask two children to take a number. *Which is the smaller number?* Attach this number to one of the teddy bears and sit him on the floor. Look together at the larger number. *What is this number?* Attach this to another teddy and position him about a metre away from the first one. In turn, the children take a number card and read it, before placing it in the correct position in relation to the teddy bears. *Does your number come between the teddies' numbers? Is your number larger or smaller than the first teddy bear's number?* When all the cards are positioned, count along the line together to check that the order is correct.

Square numbers

- *Recognising a set of numbers more or less than a given number*

Number cards (1 to 20), chalk

Draw two large squares, about a metre apart, on the playground. Label the first square 'numbers smaller than' and the second square 'numbers bigger than' and make sure that the children know which is which. Give a number card to each child and ask them to stand between the two squares. Call out a number between 1 and 20. The children look at their card, decide if their number is bigger or smaller than the one you called out, then run and stand in the correct square. Check they are correct, then repeat with other numbers.

Post-it numbers

• *Recognising numbers*
Number grid (0 to 50), Post-it notes

Let the children choose any number on the grid and help them to write it, with their name, on a Post-it note. Ask the children to help you count the numbers on the grid in order. Tell them that when they hear their number they must shout, *Stop!* and stick their note in the correct place on the number grid. Did all the children say *Stop!* in time? *Are all the notes on the correct numbers? Who has the smallest/largest number?*

Representing numerals

Creating numbers

• *Beginning to record numbers up to 10*
Finger paints, a number track (1 to 10)

Select a numeral from the number track. Demonstrate how that numeral is formed. Ask the children to draw it with their finger in the air or on a piece of paper. They then paint the number on the paper with finger paints. Let them practise the same number several times, reminding the children how to form the numeral correctly.

Painting numbers

• *Recording numbers to mark the number in a set*
Finger paints, a number track (1 to 20)

Ask the children to choose a number and identify it on the number track. They paint the same number of objects, such as rabbits, flowers, butterflies, trees, or balloons. Then ask them to finger paint their chosen numeral. Ask each child to say their number and count the objects to check that they have matched the correct numeral to the objects.

Comparing and ordering numbers

More and less

How tall are the children?

• *Comparing two quantities*

Large pieces of paper, paints, coloured paper, pencils, scissors, shoes of the same length, Blu-tack

Ask two children (one tall, one short) to lie down on a large piece of paper and draw round them. Let the children paint inside the outlines and ask them how many shoes tall they think the shorter child might be. Write down their estimates and choose one of them. Let the children draw around the shoes that many times. Cut out the shoe shapes carefully and attach them alongside the outline of the shorter child, counting the shoes and reviewing the estimate as you do so. Repeat with the outline of the taller child. Before you begin, ask the children to estimate whether they will use more or fewer shoe shapes. *Which outline needs more/less shoes? Why?*

Quick sort

• *Comparing two numbers*

Number cards (1 to 20), three hoops

Place three hoops on the floor and label them 'bigger than', 'smaller than' and 'same as'. Give each child a number card and call out a number. Ask the children to decide whether the number on their card is bigger, smaller or the same the number you called. When they have decided, the children should place their card in the appropriate hoop. Check that the children have positioned the cards correctly, then repeat.

How many in the tin?

• Beginning to know the number 1 more or 1 less
Number cards (1 to 10), a tin, 1p coins

Divide the children into pairs. Give each pair a set of cards and ask them to arrange the numbers into a track. Drop some of the coins into a tin and tell the children to listen very carefully as you do so. They should match each coin dropped with their number cards, touching the next card each time they hear a coin being dropped. When all the coins are in the tin, check that the children are touching the correct number. Take a coin out of the tin. *How many coins are in the tin now? One more or one less?* Put your finger on the correct number. Check that they have all counted back one. Repeat with different numbers of coins.

Ordering numbers

Car numbers

• Ordering numbers to 10
Number cards (0 to 9), toy cars, small 'number plates', Blu-tack

Take the children outside to look at real cars or use toy cars with number plates attached. Look at a car number plate and ask a child to find the number cards to match the numbers on the car. Read the numbers together. *Eight, one, five.* Ask the children if the numbers are in the correct order. *Which is the smallest number? Who can put the one first?* Read the numbers again. *One, eight, five. Are they in the correct order now? Which is the largest number? Is it in the correct place?* Read the numbers in the correct order. Look at another car number plate and repeat.

Three in a row

• Comparing numbers
Number cards (1 to 30)

Shuffle the cards and deal out three to each child. Ask the children to hold up their smallest number and place it in front of them. *Hold up your largest number.* Ask the children to place that one near to the smallest card, leaving a space between the two cards. Then ask them to put down their middle-sized number card. *The middle-sized number comes between the smallest and the largest numbers.* Collect in the cards and repeat with three different ones. Extend to ordering six numbers.

Adding

Counting on

Under the blanket

- *Counting on one more*

Eight soft toys, a small blanket, number cards (1 to 9)

Together, count four soft toys onto the folded blanket. *How many toys are there? Four. Who can find the card with four on it?* Fold the blanket over the toys and place the number 4 card on top of the blanket. Hold up one more toy. *If this toy gets into bed, how many will there be? Five. Four and one more make five.* Write the number sentence, 4 + 1 = 5. Reveal the four toys, count them again and add one more to make five. Repeat to make another number sum.

Penny drop

- *Counting on one more*

A small tin, several real 1p coins

With your back to the children, slowly drop five 1p coins into the tin. Encourage the children to raise a finger each time they hear a penny drop. *Can you show me with your fingers how many 1p coins are in the tin?* Tip the coins out and count them again if the children have miscounted. *If I drop one more coin into the tin, how many will there be?* Write down the number sentence and read it together.

Ten to a snake

- *Counting on one, two or three more*
- *Counting backwards*

Chalk

On the playground, draw a snake with ten segments, numbered 1 to 10. Ask each child to stand in one segment. *Jenny, where will you be if you hop onto the next number? Martin, hop on two more. Where are you now?* Continue, asking the children to hop on one, two or three more each time. Repeat, asking the children to jump backwards along the snake.

A row of toys

• *Saying the next number to a given number*
• *Counting on from a given number*

Number cards (1 to 20), twenty soft toys

Ask the children to help you place twenty soft toys in a row and then count them together. Give a child the number 10 card and ask them to place it on toy number 10. Encourage all the children to count to find this toy. *What is the next number?* Give a child the number 11 card to place on the next toy. *Which number comes before ten?* Give a child the number 9 card to place on the correct toy. Continue asking similar questions until all the toys are numbered. Choose a number, point to the toy and encourage all the children to count on from that number. Change the number frequently to maintain pace and enthusiasm.

Door numbers

• *Saying the next number to a given number*

Pictures of front doors, paper/card rectangles, paint, paintbrushes, adhesive numbers

Spend a little time discussing front doors: the colours, letter-boxes, doorbells, knockers and windows. Look at the pictures and encourage the children to think of some imaginative ideas for their own designs. Give each child a paper or card rectangle to paint a front door. Help them to write their name on the door. When the doors are dry, ask the children to hold their door and stand in a row. In number order, give each child an adhesive number to stick onto their door. *Who lives next door to James? What is his door number?* Swap around some of the doors and ask the children what has happened and how the display can be corrected. Alternatively, turn a door over and ask the children to suggest which number is displayed on the hidden door.

Finger stories

• *Counting on from a given number*

Using your fingers, tell the children some number stories, adding on or taking away numbers as the stories progress. *Can you show me six fingers?* Encourage the children to hold up all the fingers on one hand and show one finger from the other hand. *These are six little birds perched on a branch. It is a very quiet tree and two more birds join them. How many birds are there now? Six and two more make eight. Oh dear! A dog barks and all eight birds fly away. How many are left?* Write the number sentences on the board and repeat the story, relating it to the numbers on the board.

Making mistakes

• *Counting on from a given number*

Large number cards (1 to 20), a soft toy or puppet

Select a child to lay the numbers in a line on the floor. The children count as each number is placed. Show the children the toy or puppet. Explain that he is very careless at counting so they must shout *Stop!* if he makes a mistake. Starting from 1, walk the toy along the line, counting and making some deliberate mistakes. Either miss out some numbers, keeping the number sequence correct, or make mistakes with the sequence. If appropriate, start counting at different numbers.

Finding totals

Ways of making 8

• *Partitioning a set*

Chalk, large number cards (1 to 9), large operation cards ('+' and '=')

Draw two large shapes on the playground. Select a number card, e.g. 8, and choose that number of children to stand in one of the shapes. Place the 8 and '=' cards on the playground and nearby lay out the number cards less than 8. Ask two children to choose two of the cards and read out the numbers, e.g. 5 and 3. Invite a child to distribute the eight children between the two shapes to make the two sets. Place the number cards to complete the number sentence, i.e. 5 + 3 = 8. Encourage the children to combine other numbers to make 8.

Bears in the bed

• *Combining two sets*

Two small beds or boxes, ten teddy bears, number cards (1 to 9), operation cards ('+' and '=')

Ask two children to take a number card each (smaller than 6) and to place a matching number of bears in one of the beds or boxes. They then place the number cards on the beds with the '+' card between them. Read the number sentence together. *Five bears add three bears makes eight bears.* Encourage the children to count on from 5 to find the total. Place the '=' card to the right of the second bed and then the number 8 card to show the answer. Read the sentence together again. Repeat with different numbers.

Toys in hoops

• *Understanding addition as the combination of two sets*
• *Relating addition to the partitioning of a set*

Number cards (0 to 10), operation cards ('+', '='), ten soft toys, two hoops

Select a child to count out eight soft toys. *Who can put some of these eight toys in each hoop? How many are in the first hoop? How many are in the second hoop?* Ask one of the children to make the number sentence using the cards, 5 + 3 = 8. *Who can move the toys to make a new number sentence with only eight toys?* Repeat for the remaining partitions of 8, then with a different number of toys.

Teddies on plates

- *Understanding addition as the combination of two sets*
- *Relating addition to the partitioning of a set*

Paper plates, teddy counters

Divide the children into pairs and give each pair two plates. Let one child in each pair count out seven teddy counters and place them near the plates. The children then make a number sentence by placing some of their teddy counters on each plate. Ask the children in each pair to read their number sentence and write these on the board. Read out a number sentence and ask the children who have created that number sentence to raise their hands. Repeat with a different number of teddy counters.

Adding bean bags

- *Understanding addition as the partitioning of a set*

Number cards (0 to 10), operation cards ('+', '='), ten bean bags, a small hoop, a cane

Place a hoop on the floor and lie the cane a short distance away from it. Invite a child to count out seven beanbags. *How many beanbags are there? Who would like to throw as many bean bags as they can into the hoop?* Choose a child to stand behind the cane and let them throw the bean bags towards the hoop. *How many bean bags did Evie get in the hoop? Five.* Invite another child to place the number 5 card by the hoop. *How many bean bags missed the hoop? Two.* Explain how to make the number sentence. *Five (in the hoop) and two (out of the hoop) equals seven altogether.* Write it on the board, 5 + 2 = 7. Repeat with other children throwing different numbers of bean bags.

On the mat

• Understanding addition as the partitioning of a set
A mat, large number cards (1 to 10)

Place a number card, e.g. 8, on the mat. *How many children must sit on the mat?* Count out six children and ask them to sit on the mat. *Are there enough children on the mat? Are there too many or too few? Can you help me find out how many extra children we need?* Touch your head and say, *Six there already.* Then count on with your finger. *Seven, eight.* Raise two fingers as you count. *How many more do we need?* Count two more children onto the mat. Ask the children to help you check by counting that there are eight children on the mat.

One or two more than

One more bead

• Adding to a number up to 10
Number cards (1 to 10), large number cards (1 to 10), a lace, beads

Divide the children into pairs and give each pair a set of number cards, beads and a lace knotted at one end. Ask the children to lay out the cards in order to make a number track. Select one of your number cards, e.g. 4, and show the children. They thread a matching number of beads onto their lace. Ask them to point to the number on their track. *How many beads will there be if we add one more? What number is one more than four? Can you point to it on the line? What is the number? Five.* The children thread an extra bead onto the lace to check. Continue adding beads, one, two or three at a time.

How many toys?

• Finding a total by counting on
Number cards (1 to 10), a small blanket, ten soft toys

Ask the children to help you count some of the toys onto a table. Cover the toys with the blanket. *How many toys are there? Five. If I slide two more toys under the blanket, how many will there be?* Encourage the children to count on from 5. *Six, seven.* Lay out the number cards in order. *How many toys are under the blanket now? Seven. If I put one more under the blanket, how many will there be?* Count on one more along the number cards and put another toy under the blanket. Check that the numbers match. Repeat for different numbers of toys under the blanket.

Number snake

• Adding to a number up to 10

Chalk, a large imitation coin, building bricks

Draw a large snake on the playground with ten numbered segments. Ask two or three children to stand on number 1. The children take turns to toss the coin: if it lands heads, they bounce forwards one space; if it lands tails, they bounce forwards two spaces. Before they move, encourage the children to say which number they will land on. The first child to jump off the end of the snake is the winner. If appropriate, repeat starting at 10 and counting backwards down the snake.

Number grab

• Counting forwards and backwards
• Adding to a number up to 20

Number cards (1 to 20)

Sit the children in a semi-circle and arrange the number cards at random on the floor in front of them. Together count up to 20 and back to 1. Tell the children that you are going to call out a number. They should try to find the number card which is 1 more than the number you call. The first child to take the card, stand up and say the number is the winner. Repeat with other numbers and with saying the number 2 or 3 more than the one you call.

Subtracting

Counting back

Naughty toys

• *Subtracting by counting back*
Ten soft toys, a small blanket

Ask the children to help you count the ten toys onto the table. *How many toys are there? Ten.* Cover the toys with a blanket and then remove two of them. *How many toys have come out of bed? Two. Can you show me with your fingers the two naughty toys that didn't stay in bed? How many were there in bed to begin with? Put the ten in your head and count back two with your fingers. Ten in your head, bend down one finger to make nine, bend down the second finger to make eight. There are eight toys left in the bed.* Repeat with other numbers.

Bean bag basket

• *Counting back to find the remainder*
Large number cards (1 to 5), fifteen bean bags, a basket

Together, count the bean bags into the basket. Shuffle the cards and place them face down in a pile on the floor. Invite a child to reveal the top card and read the number. *Can you take that number of bean bags out of the basket?* Ask a child to count them out onto the floor. *I wonder how many are left in the basket? We can find out by counting back four from fifteen. Put fifteen in your head and touch each beanbag as you count back. Fourteen, thirteen, twelve, eleven.* Ask a child to check that there are 11 left by counting out the remaining bean bags from the basket. Ask the children to show four fingers. *Put fifteen in your head and count back four saying, fourteen, thirteen, twelve, eleven, as you bend down your fingers, one at a time.* Put all the beanbags back in the basket and repeat with another number.

Taking away

Parking spaces

• *Removing a small number of objects from a larger number*
A number track (1 to 20), toy cars, a dice

Lay out the number track on the table. *This is a carpark.* Ask the children to place a toy car on each space. *How many cars are in the car park? Twenty.* Ask a child to roll the dice. *How many spots are showing? Four. Four cars drive out of the carpark. How many will be left?* (If the total number is small, ask the children to count back the number using their fingers before removing the cars.) *How many empty spaces are there? How many cars need to drive back in to fill the car park?* Rearrange the cars and repeat.

Money

Recognising coins

Coin collection

• *Recognising coins*

Real coins (1p, 2p, 5p, 10p, 20p, 50p, £1, £2 as appropriate), classroom objects priced with each coin value, a box, interlocking cubes

Show the children each type of coin and ensure that they can identify each one. Divide the children into pairs. Give each pair one of each coin and ask them to line up the coins in order of value. Take a priced object out of the box, show it to the children and let them read the price. The first child from each pair to find the correct coin to buy the object wins a cube. Continue for the remaining objects. The winner in each pair is the child with the most cubes.

Shoe box shop

• *Recognising coins*

A shoe box, classroom objects, price labels, coins (1p, 2p, 5p, 10p, 20p, 50p, £1, £2 as appropriate)

Divide the children into small groups and ask them to select classroom objects to put into their shoe box. Help them to label each object with a coin value. Taking turns to be the customers and the shopkeeper, the children buy an object in the shoe box and pay for it with the correct value coin.

Penny match

• *Beginning to match each coin to its appropriate number of 1p coins*

Demostration coins (1p, 2p, 5p, 10p, 20p), 1p coins

Divide the children into pairs. Ask each child to count out ten 1p coins. *How many coins does each pair have altogether?* Encourage the children to count the coins together. As they count, make sure that the children touch and move the coins. Place the demonstration coins on the floor, touch each one and ask the children to name them. Hold one of them up, e.g. 5p. *How many 1p coins do I need to make 5p? Five. Can you count out five 1p coins?* Repeat with the other coin values.

Coin swap

• Beginning to match each coin to its appropriate number of 1p coins
Coins (1p, 2p, 5p, 10p)

Divide the children into pairs. For each pair, give one child seventeen 1p coins and the other several 2p, 5p, and 10p coins. Explain that those with just the 1p coins have to swap them for coins of a higher value. Invite the child with the larger value coins to hold one up and ask for that number of 1p coins. *Oliver has a 5p coin. How many 1p coins must Ella give him?* When the other child has counted out five 1p coins, she swaps them for the 5p coin. The children continue until they have swapped all their coins. Let the children repeat the activity, changing roles.

Using coins

Coin tower

• Solving simple addition and subtraction problems using money
1p coins, large building bricks, Blu-tack

Ask a child to build a tower of ten bricks. *How many bricks are in the tower? If each brick costs 1p, how much would we need to pay for this tower?* Attach a 1p coin to each brick with Blu-tack and count together to find how much the tower is worth. *If each brick costs 2p, how much would the tower cost? How much more will we need to attach to this brick?* Ask the children to attach an extra penny to each brick. Count the coins together, whispering *1p*, saying *2p*, whispering *3p*, saying *4p*, etc. Repeat for different-sized towers.

Bead values

• Counting up to ten coins
1p coins, beads, laces, a one-minute sand timer

Give each child a lace with a knot at one end and some beads. Ask the children to estimate how many beads they think they will be able to thread onto the lace in one minute. Write down their estimates. Ask the children to thread the beads and activate the timer. At the end of one minute, let them count how many beads are on the lace. The children then count out the number of 1p coins to match the number of beads on their lace. *Who has the most/least amount of money for their bead string?*

Penny sweets

• *Beginning to match each coin to its appropriate number of 1p coins*
Several 1p coins, price labels, dough, paint, varnish
Ask the children to make pretend sweets in a variety of shapes (e.g. cubes, cylinders, cuboids, etc) using dough. Ask them to sort the sweets into shapes and see if they can name each shape. Leave the sweets to dry thoroughly. (It is important that they are not too large and are allowed to they dry very slowly, or they will fall apart.) When the shapes are dry, let the children paint them. When the paint is dry, varnish the shapes. Price the different-shaped sweets, helping the children to write the labels. Invite a child to be the shopkeeper and ask each child in turn to buy two sweets. Explain that they need to pay for the sweets with the correct number of 1p coins.

How much do the bears cost?

• *Solving simple addition and subtraction problems using money*
Teddy counters, 1p coins
Divide the children into pairs and give each pair about four teddy counters and at least twelve 1p coins. Explain that one teddy counter costs 3p. Ask how much two teddies would cost. Encourage the children to put down two teddies and place three 1p coins in front of each one. Ask them to count how much the teddies cost altogether. Help them to buy another teddy counter. *How much will three teddies cost?* Continue buying the teddy counters, ensuring that the children place the correct number of coins by each one. Ask the children to take away the teddy counters one at a time and tell you how much the remaining teddies cost.

Measures

Length

As long as your shoe

• *Comparing the length of three objects*

Dough or Plasticine, children's shoes

Ask the children to roll out three dough snakes – one that is longer than their shoe, one that is shorter and one that is exactly the same length as their shoe. Encourage them to arrange the dough snakes in order and to talk about longest, shortest and middle-sized snakes.

Threading beads

• *Comparing lengths*

Laces, beads, a one-minute sand timer

Divide the children into small groups and give each child a lace knotted at one end. Ask the children to thread as many beads as possible onto the lace while the sand runs through the timer. Invite the children to sit in pairs and compare their lengths of beads by laying them next to each other. Ask the children with the shorter length of beads to stand up and hold up their lace, then repeat with the children with the longer laces.

As tall as possible

• *Comparing tall and short*

Interlocking cubes, a one-minute sand timer

Give each child some cubes and ask them to make as tall a tower as possible in one minute. Let the children sit in pairs to compare the heights of the towers they have built. You may need to remind them that to compare the heights the towers must be held upright on a level base. Ask the child with the shorter tower in each pair to put up their hand. Repeat for the taller tower. If any pairs have made towers which are exactly the same height, ask them to swap partners.

Long socks

• *Beginning to measure lengths using a non-standard unit*

Three socks of different lengths, teddy counters

Ask the children to help you put the socks in order of length. Ensure that they can point to the longest, shortest and middle-length sock. Show the children a teddy counter and ask them to estimate the length in teddy counters of the shortest sock. Choose one of the estimates and place that number of counters along the sock, counting as they are placed. Stop half-way to check how many counters have been used. *Do you think we will need all the teddies that we guessed? How many more do you think we will use?* Place the remaining counters to measure the sock. *How many teddies did we use? Will we need more teddies, fewer teddies or the same number to measure the middle-length sock?* Repeat for the longest sock.

Tubby teddies

• *Beginning to measure lengths using a non-standard unit*

Three teddy bears with different girths, strips of paper, teddy counters, scissors

Show the children the three teddy bears and ask if they are all the same 'fatness'. Let the children arrange them in order, fattest to thinnest. Discuss how you might measure the 'fatness' of the teddies. Explain that as it is difficult to measure around the teddies' tummies with counters, you are going to use strips of paper and measure their lengths. Invite a child to measure around the thinnest teddy with a strip of paper. Cut the strip and write 'thinnest teddy' on it. Repeat for the other teddies. Compare the lengths of the strips. *Did we put the teddies in the correct order of 'fatness'?* Choose a child to place teddy counters along the shortest strip. Count the teddy counters and write the measurement on the strip. Ask if the medium-sized bear will need more, the same or fewer teddy counters to measure his strip. Repeat for each bear, then compare the length in teddy counters for each strip to check that the original 'fatness' order was correct.

Snakes alive!

• *Comparing the lengths of two or three objects*

Number cards (8 to 16), dough or Plasticine, rolling pins, interlocking cubes

Ask the children to choose a number card, take that many cubes and make a tower with them. Give each child a lump of dough or Plasticine and ask them to roll it out to make a snake exactly the same length as their tower. *Who has the longest snake? How can we find out?* Repeat for the shortest snake. Ask the children to sit in threes to compare their snakes. Can they put them in order and say which is the longest, shortest and middle-length snake?

Headbands

• *Beginning to estimate a length*

Strips of card, potato printers, paint, a stapler

For each child, cut a strip of card to measure around their head, leaving a little extra for an overlap. Show them the potato printers. *About how many potato prints do you think will you need to decorate along your strip?* Make a note of each child's estimate. Show the children how to print and explain that they should not overlap the prints or leave spaces between them. Invite them to print along their headband and encourage them to count each print. *How many prints did you make? Did you estimate too many, too few or the correct number? Who has the most prints on their headband?* When the paint is dry, staple the ends together to complete the headband and let the children wear them.

How tall is the adult?

• *Beginning to estimate a height*
• *Measuring a length using a non-standard unit*

A long length of paper (e.g. wallpaper), felt-tipped pens, scissors, an adult's shoe, coloured paper, paints, collage materials

Roll out the paper on the floor and ask an adult to lie on it. Ask the children to draw carefully around the adult. Cut out the shape and show the children the shoe. *About how many of these shoes long is the adult?* Write the estimates on the board. Ask the children to draw round and cut out some shoe shapes. Invite two children to place the shoe shapes half-way up the body shape. *How many shoes high is the adult up to here? How many more shoe shapes do you think we will need? Will we need as many as our estimate?* Continue until the full length has been measured. *How many shoes long is our adult?* Let the children decorate the body shape and then display it with its height in shoes. Discuss how tall the adult is compared with other people and objects.

How far can you jump?

• *Beginning to estimate a length*
• *Measuring a length using a non-standard unit*

Chalk, crayons, pencils or other suitable measuring apparatus, a large sheet of paper

Show the children the pencils and ask them how far they think they can jump if the jump is measured in pencils. Draw a chalk line across the playground and ask a child to jump from the line as far as they can. Mark where they land and write their name by the mark. Continue until all the children have jumped. Show the children how to place the pencils together, end to end, and then encourage them to measure their jump using the pencils. Help them to write down their name and the length of their jump in pencils. Look at the results. *Who had the longest jump? How do we know?*

Weight

Heavy shoes

• *Comparing heavy and light objects*

Several shoes, a bucket balance

Ask a child to choose two different shoes and to compare the weights in their hands. *Which shoe do you think is the heavier? Which is the lighter?* Invite another child to compare the shoes. *Which shoe will go down in the bucket? Why? Which shoe will go up in the bucket? Why?* Check the children's guesses using the bucket balance. Repeat with two other shoes.

Apple balance

• *Beginning to measure weights on scales using non-standard units*

A bag of small apples, balance scales, large teddy counters

Choose an apple. *What will happen if you put the apple into this pan? Why will it go down? About how many of these teddies do you think will balance with the apple?* Choose one of the children's estimates and count out that number of counters. Invite a child to place one teddy at a time into the opposite pan on the scales. As the child places the teddies, ask several times if the apple and the teddies are balancing. *How do you know that they are not balancing? What must we do to make the pans balance?* Choose a smaller/larger apple and repeat the activity.

Weighing dough

• *Comparing heavy and light objects*
• *Beginning to measure weights on scales using non-standard units*

Balance scales, large teddy counters, dough

Make a dough ball to balance with twelve large teddy counters and show it to the children. In pairs, ask the children to count twelve counters into one pan of the scales and then to make a dough ball to make the scales balance. Remind them that they cannot change the number of counters; they can only add or take away from the dough. Discuss how to balance the dough. Make sure that the children realise that if the dough is too heavy, some needs to be removed, and if it is too light they need to add some more. Repeat for a different number of teddy counters.

Capacity

Mug or cup?

• *Comparing the capacity of two containers*
A mug, a cup, a tray, a jug of water

Hold up the cup and the mug and ask the children which one will hold the most water. *Why do you think the mug will hold most? How can we find out?* Invite a child to fill the mug with water over a tray. *What do you think will happen if I pour the mug of water into the empty cup? Why do you think it will spill over the top?* Ask one of the children to try it out. *What will happen if we pour the water back into the mug?* Invite another child to investigate. *Why doesn't the water come up to the top of the mug?*

Cup of tea?

• *Comparing the capacity of two containers*
• *Beginning to understand the vocabulary of capacity*
A teapot, several transparent plastic cups, a tray, a jug of water, food colouring

Add a few drops of food colouring to the water. Fill the teapot with water and ask the children how many cups they think can be filled from the teapot. Make a note of their estimates and count out one of their estimated numbers of cups onto the tray. Invite a child to pour water from the teapot into a cup. *Is the cup full? How do you know?* Ask another child to fill the next cup and repeat the questioning. When the teapot is about half full, ask the children if it is empty yet. *How many cups have we filled already? How many more do you think we will fill?* Let the children continue until the teapot is empty. *How many cups did we fill with the teapot? Did anyone estimate the correct number of cups?* Compare the answer with the children's estimates to see if anyone guessed correctly.

Time

Speed printing

• *Counting the number of times something happens in one minute*
A one-minute sand timer, paint, printers (sponge, potatoes or wooden blocks)
Give each child a sheet of paper, some paint and a printer. Set the timer and ask the children to print as many shapes as they can on the paper before the sand runs out. At the end of the minute, the children count their prints. *Who has made the most prints?*

Clap in time

• *Counting the number of times something happens in one minute*
A one-minute sand timer
Set the timer and count together as you clap. Try to count as near as possible to 60 before the sand runs out.

On the hour

• *Reading and setting the time to the hour*
An analogue clock with movable hands
Remind the children of what each hand on a clock shows. Set the clock to 1 o'clock and slowly turn the knob, asking the children to watch the clock hands carefully. Tell the children to shout *Stop!* when the long hand has travelled all the way around and back to the top of the clock. Repeat for the other hours, stopping at each o'clock time.

What's the time Mr Wolf?

• *Reading and setting the time to the hour*
An analogue clock with movable hands
Secretly set the clock to an o'clock time. Encourage the children to ask, *What's the time Mr Wolf?* Show them the clock and ask them to say the o'clock time, then all clap that number of times. Repeat for other o'clock times. Repeat the activity outside with the children standing away from you as they call out, *What's the time Mr Wolf?* Show them the clock and encourage them to take that number of paces forwards. When the children are quite close to you, shout *Dinnertime!* and chase them away.

The days go on and on!

• *Ordering the days of the week*
Sit the children in a circle. Say a day of the week, point to a child and ask them to say the following day. Encourage the children to say the other days of the week in order. As each child says a day, they stretch out their legs and pull them back in again. Carry on round and round the circle until each child has had at least three turns.

What happened when?

• *Beginning to understand today, tomorrow and yesterday*
Large labels ('Monday', 'Tuesday', 'Wednesday', 'Thursday', 'Friday', 'Saturday', 'Sunday'), small labels ('yesterday', 'today', 'tomorrow')
Display the small labels. *What day is it today? Who can find 'Tuesday' and pin it up under 'today'? What day will it be tomorrow? Who can find and pin up 'Wednesday'?* Repeat for 'yesterday'. Ask the children to talk about something significant that happens on those three days. Ask the children to draw a picture for each section then describe them. *Yesterday Ainsley went swimming. Tomorrow Abigail will be five. Today Toby is going to tea with Ravi.*

Shape and space

2-d shape

Coloured shapes

• *Recognising 2-d shapes*
Large 2-d shapes, paints, a large sheet of paper
Give each child a large sheet of paper and a variety of 2-d shapes. Ask the children to draw carefully around some of the shapes and to paint the shapes using a different colour for each one.

Make a cat

• *Naming and recognising 2-d shapes*
2-d shapes, card, scissors, glue, adhesive shapes, string, large and small plates
Help the children to make a cat using 2-d shapes. Draw round the plates to make a large and a small circle from card. Cut them out and put them together to make a head and body. Glue them onto a sheet of paper. Ask the children to find circles to use as eyes, and triangles to use for ears and a nose, then stick them to the cat. Finish the cat by adding a length of string for its tail. Can the children count how many of each different type of shape they have used?

Get into shapes

• *Beginning to name rectangles and triangles*
• *Rehearsing naming squares and circles*
Chalk
Draw three rectangles, circles, squares and triangles on the playground. Call out the name of a shape. How quickly can the children step into the correct shape? Make the activity more difficult by saying properties of shapes. *Step into a three-sided shape/a four-sided shape/a shape with four corners/a shape with a curved side.*

Make a shape

• *Beginning to name rectangles and triangles*
• *Rehearsing naming squares and circles*
Six straws for each child (four the same length and two shorter or longer ones), lengths of string or wool
Give each child six straws and a length of string or wool. Say the name of a shape and encourage the children to make the shape as quickly as possible with the apparatus. They should fit the straws together to make shapes with straight sides and use the string or wool to make circles. Can the children tell you something about the shape they have made?

3-d shape

Making cubes and cuboids

• *Recognising and naming a cube*
• *Beginning to recognise a cuboid*

Cubes and cuboids, Polydron squares and oblongs

Put the 3-d shapes and Polydron on the table. *Can you hold up a cube? How many faces has the cube? What shape are the faces? How many Polydron squares will you need to make a cube?* Ask the children to fit some Polydron squares together to make a cube. *How many squares did you use to make your cube?* Then ask the children to hold up a cuboid. *How many faces has the cuboid? Are there any square faces? How many square faces are there? Does your cuboid have any oblong faces? How many?* (Some cuboids have two square faces, some have four, and some have all oblong faces.) Ask the children to make a cuboid with the Polydron shapes.

A cube cat

• *Recognising and naming a cube*

Cube nets, sticky tape, odd scraps of paper, scissors, glue, small 2-d shapes

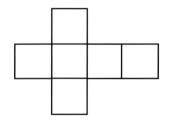

Give each child a cube net and help them fold it up and stick the edges together with sticky tape. Using the small 2-d shapes, encourage the children to cut out triangle shapes for ears and a nose, and circles for eyes. Let the children glue the shapes to the cube and then add long strips of paper for whiskers. Finally, help them to cut round and round a circle, starting from the edge to form a spiral, and give their cat a long curly tail.

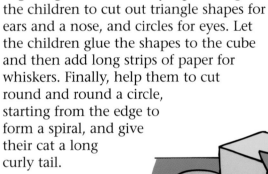

Mr or Mrs Cuboid

• *Beginning to recognise a cuboid*

A variety of small boxes, glue, pegs, paint, coloured paper, wool, tissue, strips of card, small 2-d shapes, scissors, sticky tape

In advance, prepare some cuboid-shaped boxes for the children to decorate and turn into characters. Pull the boxes apart along the seams. Turn them inside out and re-glue the seams, using pegs to hold the sides together. Give each child a box and ask them to turn it into Mr or Mrs Cuboid. Encourage them to paint their cuboid, then use small 2-d shapes as templates for facial features, e.g. circles for eyes, a rectangle for a mouth and a triangle for a nose. Suggest that they fold strips of cards like a concertina to use as legs and arms and cut out the shapes of boots and mittens to attach to the ends. They could also use strips of torn tissue of pieces of wool for hair. Display the characters by hanging them from the ceiling.

Fat and thin mice

• *Beginning to name cones*

3-d cones, thin card, a saucer, coloured paper, scissors, a small stapler, glue, adhesive shapes, pipe cleaners

Show the children the cones and explain that they have one curved face and one flat circular face. Tell them that they are going to use a half circle of card to make the curved shape of a cone and then turn it into a mouse. Ask the children to draw a circle on the card by drawing around a saucer and then cut out the circle carefully. Help them to fold the circle in half and cut along the folded line to make two semi-circles. Help the children to join the straight edges of one semi-circle together to make a cone and staple them, bearing in mind that the more the edges are overlapped, the thinner the eventual mouse will. Encourage them to use both semi-circles to make one thin and one fat mouse. Let the children complete the mice using small circles cut into two semi-circles for ears, circles for eyes, a triangle for a nose, pipe cleaners for whiskers and tail. *Who has made the thinnest/fattest mouse?*

A pyramid pet

• *Beginning to name pyramids*

Polydron, 3-d triangular pyramids, triangles, card, sticky tape, scraps of coloured paper, scissors, glue

Show the children the 3-d triangular pyramids and ask them how many faces they have. *What shape are the faces? What shape Polydron will you need to make the pyramid? How many triangles will you need?* Ask the children to use four triangular Polydron shapes to make the net of a pyramid. Using some card, they then draw around the net and cut out the shape. Help the children to fold along the edges of the triangles and put the pyramid together, holding the edges together with sticky tape. Encourage the children to decorate the faces of their pyramid to turn it into a pet.

Patterns

Repeating patterns

- *Recognising and recreating simple patterns*
- *Recognising and naming 2-d shapes*

Large 2-d circles and squares

Ask a child to choose a shape. *What shape is this? How do you know it is a circle?* Place it on the table. Ask another child to select a different shape (a square) and to describe and name it. Place the square next to the circle. Explain to the children that they are going to make a repeating pattern. Ask a third child to pick up a circle and place it next to the square. Read the beginning of the pattern together. *Circle, square, circle. Which shape will come next? A square.* Continue making the pattern, asking the children to say the name of each shape as it is added to pattern. Repeat with a different pattern, then try introducing a third shape, e.g. a triangle.

A decorative border

- *Recognising and creating patterns*
- *Beginning to name rectangles and triangles*
- *Rehearsing naming squares and circles*

Sponge or potato printers (rectangles, triangles, squares, circles), long sheets of paper, paint, paintbrushes

Ask the children for suggestions for a repeating shape pattern to decorate the edge of a display board, e.g. a red triangle, a blue square, a red circle. Show the children how to print with the sponges or potatoes. Encourage the children to make their own pattern and let them print it on long sheets of paper. When they have finished, ask them to name the shapes they have used and check that they are correct. Use the patterns to decorate the classroom.

Position

Rows of toys

- *Using the language of position*
- *Placing objects in given positions in relation to each other*

Six different soft toys

Ask a child to position the toys in a row one behind each other. *Which toy is behind the teddy? Which toy is in front of the teddy? Can you put the elephant between the teddy and the giraffe?*
Can you sit the giraffe beside the elephant? Continue with similar questions.

Where are the teddies?

• *Placing objects in given positions in relation to each other*

Four different-coloured teddy counters, a sheet of paper, a small cloth or a handkerchief

Give each pair of children four teddy counters and give them instructions for placing them. *Put three bears under the paper and one on top of the paper. Put all the teddies beside the cloth. Put the teddies in a line in this order: red, blue, green, yellow. Hold up the teddy that is behind the red teddy. Hold up the first teddy. Put the blue teddy in front of the red teddy. Which teddy is first now?* Ask the children to describe the positions of the different-coloured teddy counters.

Direction

Follow the pathway

• *Beginning to use the language of direction*
• *Travelling in given directions in relation to a starting point*

Chalk or lengths of rope

Draw a chalk pathway with right-angled corners on the playground or lay out lengths of rope to make one. Ask a child to stand at the start of the pathway and let the other children take turns to give them instructions for following the path. *Move three steps forwards, turn towards the car park, take five steps forwards, turn to face left.* The children should continue giving instructions until the end of the path has been reached. Repeat, choosing other children to follow the path. Repeat, giving the children instructions for following the pathway in the reverse direction.

Which way to ...?

• *Beginning to use the language of direction*

A large sheet of paper or a road layout, toy cars

Draw a simple road map with landmarks on the paper or use a printed road layout. Let the children look closely at it. Ask them for suggestions about making a journey, e.g. taking the car from the garage to the supermarket. Invite them to explain how they would make that journey, describing what landmarks they would pass and using directional language correctly. *Take the car out of the garage and turn left. Go past the school and the church. Stop at the traffic lights and turn right into the supermarket car park*. The children can move the car along the map as they describe the journey. Repeat for different journeys.